Little Miss Muffet

and

Mosquito One, Mosquito Two

Illustrated by Lynne Willey

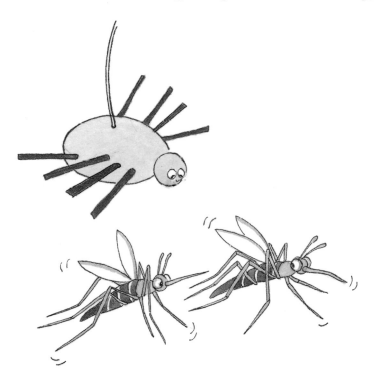

Little Miss Muffet

Little Miss Muffet
sat on a tuffet

eating her curds and whey.

There came a big spider
who sat down beside her

4

and frightened Miss Muffet away.

Mosquito One, Mosquito Two

Mosquito one,
mosquito two.

Mosquito jump
in de ole man shoe.

Little Miss Muffet

Little Miss Muffet
sat on a tuffet
eating her curds and whey.
There came a big spider
who sat down beside her
and frightened Miss Muffet away.

Mosquito One, Mosquito Two

Mosquito one,
mosquito two.

Mosquito jump
in de ole man shoe.